Texas and Texans

Texas Geography Skills

D1226017

GLENCOE

Macmillan/McGraw–Hill

Lake Forest, Illinois   Columbus, Ohio   Mission Hills, California   Peoria, Illinois

TO THE TEACHER

Texas Geography Skills is a collection of skill activities that will expand student understanding of Texas geography. The booklet has 33 activities, one for each chapter of *Texas and Texans*. Each activity is based on one of the five themes of geography: Location, Place, Movement, Regions, and Human-Environment Interaction.

Each skill activity begins with a brief introduction that sets the scene for the student. The introduction is followed by complete directions, the activity, and questions. Answers to the questions are provided in the back of this booklet.

CREATING A CUSTOMIZED FILE

The individual booklets supplied in the **Teacher's Classroom Resources** provide a wide variety of supplemental materials to enhance and enliven the teaching of Texas history. These resources appear as individual booklets in a carryall file box.

There are a variety of ways to organize *Texas and Texans* classroom resources. Three alternative ways of creating your own files are given below.

- **Organize all resources by category** (all enrichment readings, all Texas geography activities, all tests, etc., filed separately)
- **Organize by category and chapter** (all Chapter 1 activities, all Chapter 1 tests, all Chapter 1 transparencies, etc.)
- **Organize resources sequentially by lesson or section** (activities, quizzes, study guides for Chapter 1, Section 1; Chapter 1, Section 2; etc.)

Regardless of the organization you use, you can pull out individual activity sheets from the **Teacher's Classroom Resources** booklets for your files, or you may photocopy directly from the booklet and file the photocopies. You will then be able to keep the original booklets intact in their carryall box or in a safe place.

Send all inquiries to:
GLENCOE DIVISION
Macmillan/McGraw-Hill
936 Eastwind Drive
Westerville, Ohio 43081-3374

ISBN 0-02-822579-1

Printed in the United States of America

1 2 3 4 5 6 7 8 9 MAL 99 98 97 96 95 94 93 92

Table of Contents

Texas Geography Skill 1

LOCATION: Reading Map Legends

Cartographers, or mapmakers, use symbols to present information on a map. The map legend, or key, explains the symbols. Maps usually also have a scale, which is used to measure the distance between two points. A compass rose on a map shows the primary directions: north, south, east, and west. Sometimes the compass rose will also show intermediate directions: northwest, northeast, southwest, and southeast.

Directions   Study the outline map below, then answer the questions that follow.

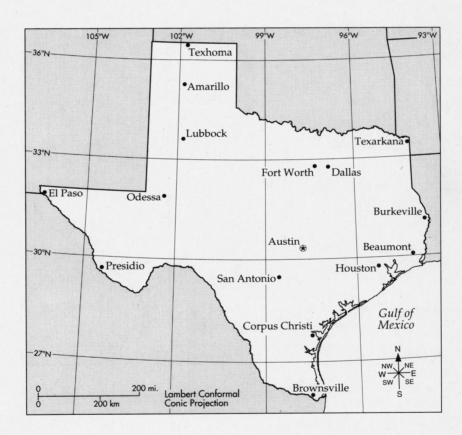

1. Houston is which direction from El Paso? _____

2. Which direction is Amarillo from Lubbock? _____

3. Odessa is which direction from Corpus Christi? _____

4. About how many miles is it from Brownsville to Austin? _____

5. About how many miles is it from Texarkana to El Paso? _____

6. About how many miles is it from Fort Worth to Austin? _____

Texas Geography Skill 2

PLACE: Rivers and Lakes of Texas

There are more than 40 rivers and thousands of small streams in Texas. Three rivers help to form the state's borders. By contrast, there are relatively few natural lakes. Lakes formed from building dams across rivers—called reservoirs—provide water for electrical power plants, irrigation, and recreation.

Directions   Study the outline map below. Next match the following rivers and lakes with their corresponding letter on the map.

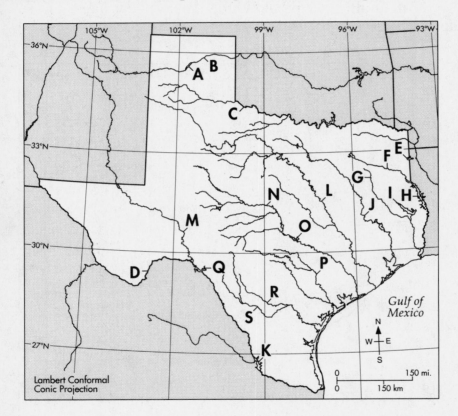

Rivers

1. Rio Grande _____   **2.** Nueces _____   **3.** Guadalupe _____   **4.** Frio _____

5. Colorado _____   **6.** Brazos _____   **7.** Trinity _____   **8.** Neches _____

9. Sabine _____   **10.** Red _____   **11.** Pecos _____   **12.** Canadian _____

Lakes and Reservoirs

13. Caddo Lake _____   **14.** Amistad Reservoir _____   **15.** Toledo Bend Reservoir _____   **16.** Lake Meredith _____   **17.** Lake Travis _____

18. Falcon Reservoir _____   **19.** Sam Rayburn Reservoir _____

Texas Geography Skill 3

REGIONS: Natural Regions of Texas

The natural regions of Texas are part of three North American natural regions, the Coastal Plain, the Continental Interior Plain, and the Western Mountains and Basins. Within Texas, there are four natural regions: the Coastal Plains, the North Central Plains, the Great Plains, and the Mountains and Basins.

Directions   Study the map below. Complete the chart that follows using information from the map and your textbook.

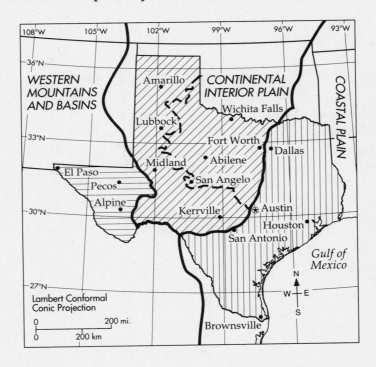

North American Region	Texas Region	Major Cities
Western Mountains and Basins		
Continental Interior Plain		
Coastal Plain		

Texas Geography Skill 4

LOCATION: Native American Groups

The Native American peoples who occupied Texas at the time of European exploration did not have precise boundaries for their lands. Maps can help you understand the location of these peoples in relation to one another and to specific places.

Directions Using your textbook and library resources, complete the map of Texas below.

1. In the upper left, draw a symbol that shows the directions: north, south, east, and west.
2. Locate and label the areas covered by the four major cultural groups: Southeastern, Puebloan, Gulf, and Plains. Draw a dotted line that shows imaginary boundaries separating these cultural groups.

3. Locate and label the areas where these Native American peoples lived: Caddoes, Jumanos, Wichitas, Coahuiltecans, Karankawas, Comanches, Kiowas.
4. Show with symbols whether each of these nations obtained food primarily through hunting, fishing, foraging, or farming. Draw a map legend to the right of the map that explains your symbols.

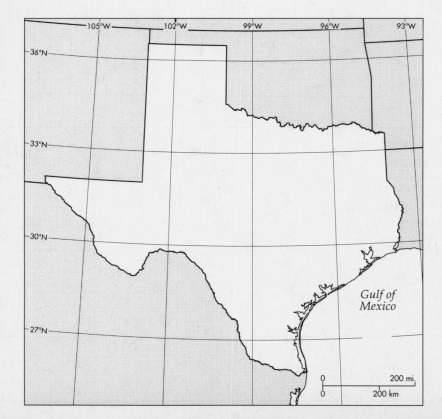

Texas Geography Skill 5

HUMAN-ENVIRONMENT INTERACTION:
Routes of European Explorers

Soon after Spain established colonies in the Americas, explorers made their way into Texas. Descriptions they provided of the land's physical features, such as soil, water, plants, and animals as well as the Native Americans they encountered, help to determine the routes they followed.

Directions Study the outline map of present-day Texas below. Then using the map and your textbook, answer the questions that follow.

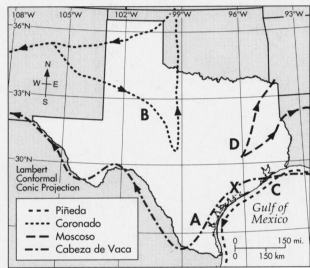

1. The explorer marked by Route A is _____ .

2. The explorer marked by Route B is _____ .

3. The explorer marked by Route C is _____ .

4. Three Native American peoples that explorer A might have met were the

   _____ , _____ , and the _____ .

5. The route of explorer D was within the land of the _____ peoples.

6. The letter X marks the approximate spot where a _____ was built by

   the French explorer _____ .

7. Explorer D crossed the _____ region, perhaps as far as the
   Brazos River.

8. Explorer C surveyed the Texas _____ .

9. Explorer B crossed a great ravine, probably the _____ .

Texas Geography Skill 6

LOCATION: Early Spanish Settlements

The Spanish began to settle in Texas only after the French claimed Texas lands. Missionaries, who hoped to convert the Native Americans to Christianity, began the first Spanish settlements. The missionaries were followed by soldiers and civilian settlers.

Directions   Study the map and the numbered description of settlements below. Complete the chart that follows using the numbered descriptions, information from the map, and your textbook.

Description of Settlements

1. founded as a halfway station
2. founded to serve the Apaches
3. first capital of Texas

4. first mission in East Texas
5. first permanent European settlement in Texas

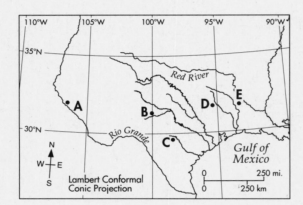

Number	Settlement Name	Map Letter	Date Founded	Nearest River
1				
2				
3				
4				
5				

Texas Geography Skills

Texas Geography Skill 7

REGIONS: The Adams-Onís Treaty

The Adams-Onís Treaty, signed in 1819, resolved a number of issues between the United States and Spain. The United States received Florida from Spain but gave up its claim to Texas.

Directions   Read the description of the border between the United States and Spanish lands set in the Adams-Onís Treaty. Then using the map below, mark the boundary with a pencil.

The boundary began at the mouth of the Sabine River. From there it moved north along the west bank to the 32nd parallel. From this point the boundary went due north until it met the Red River. At the Red River the boundary turned west and moved upstream along the south bank until it reached the 100th meridian. At this point the boundary ran due north again, until it met the Arkansas River.

At the Arkansas River the boundary turned west again, and moved along the south bank until it reached its headwaters (in the Rocky Mountains). From the headwaters a line was to be drawn due north or south to the 42nd parallel. From this point the boundary extended west along the parallel to the Pacific Ocean.

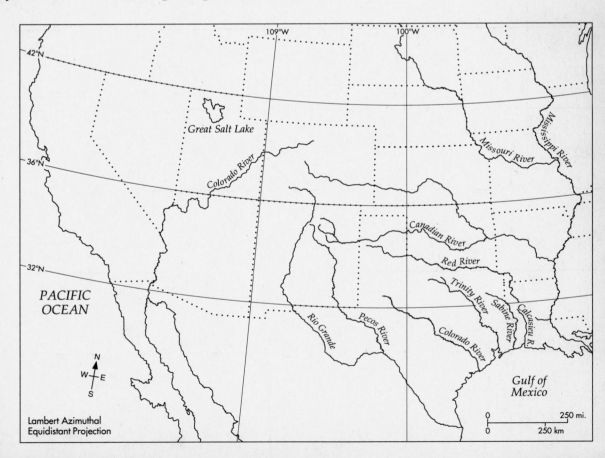

Texas Geography Skill 8

LOCATION: Austin's Land Grants

In the 1820s Mexican officials granted several persons the right to establish colonies in Texas. Stephen F. Austin was the most successful of the empresarios. He received five grants and brought thousands of families to Texas.

Directions Using your textbook, complete the chart below by providing the missing information.

LAND GRANTS OF STEPHEN F. AUSTIN, 1823–1831

Date of Grant	Relative Location of Colony	Number of Families Settled
1823		
1825		
1827		
1828		
1831		

Texas Geography Skill 9

HUMAN-ENVIRONMENT INTERACTION:
The Fredonian Revolt

One of the first clashes between Texas colonists and Mexican authorities came in East Texas. After a dispute over land claims, empresario Haden Edwards led the short-lived Republic of Fredonia near Nacogdoches. Edwards wanted to make Texas independent from Mexico.

Directions   The map of East Texas below shows the boundaries of Edwards's land grant. Use your textbook to match the letters on the map with the locations listed below. Then answer the questions that follow.

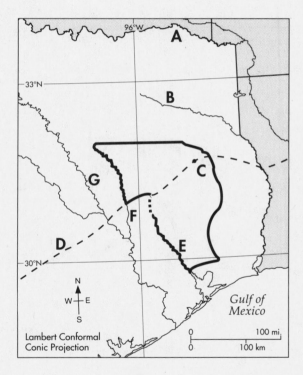

1. _____ Red River

2. _____ Sabine River

3. _____ San Jacinto River

4. _____ Navasota River

5. _____ Nacogdoches

6. _____ Brazos River

7. _____ San Antonio-Nacogdoches Road

8. About how far is Nacogdoches from the Louisiana border? _____

9. Given the close location of Edwards's grant to the United States, what effect do you

think the Fredonian Revolt had on Mexican officials? _____

_____

Texas Geography Skill 10

PLACE: Revolutionary Towns

Several villages and towns played an important role in the Texas Revolution. Some towns were the site of fighting against Mexican troops. In others, meetings were held to decide on what political actions to take.

Directions   Study the outline map, then read through the description of settlements on the left. Using information from your textbook, write the name of the settlement in the blank space provided, followed by the correct letter from the map.

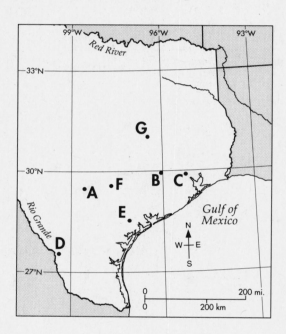

Description	Name	Map Letter
1. "Lexington of Texas"	_____	____
2. Defeat of Mexicans by 50 Texans in a brief battle	_____	____
3. Site of the Consultation of 1835	_____	____
4. Defeat of Cós's army	_____	____
5. Site where Santa Anna's army entered into Texas	_____	____
6. Second site of the *ad interim* government	_____	____
7. Site of the Convention of 1836	_____	____

Texas Geography Skill 11

MOVEMENT: Santa Anna's Advance

The Texas Revolution lasted only a few months. Many Texans were caught off guard by the rapid advance of the Mexican army and its quick victories at the Alamo and Goliad.

Directions   Using your textbook, write the date on which each of the following events took place in the blank provided. Then arrange the events in chronological order by writing them in the correct space on the time line.

_____ **1.** Fall of the Alamo

_____ **2.** First appearance of Santa Anna's troops at San Antonio

_____ **3.** Travis's last appeal to the Convention of 1836

_____ **4.** Execution of Fannin and many of his soldiers

_____ **5.** Battle of Coleto

_____ **6.** Battle of Refugio

_____ **7.** Arrival of Travis at the Alamo garrison

_____ **8.** Defeat at San Patricio

_____ **9.** Bowie ordered to the Alamo by Houston

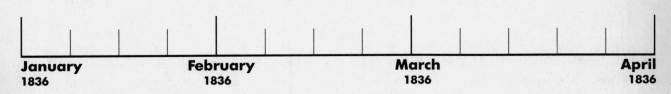

January
1836

February
1836

March
1836

April
1836

Texas Geography Skill 12

PLACE: The Runaway Scrape

The advance of Santa Anna's army after the fall of the Alamo sent many Texans fleeing for their lives. Families rushed for safety, taking with them only essential supplies. Several of Houston's soldiers deserted for a brief time in order to help their families escape. Spring rains had turned the trails into mud and flooded the rivers, making the escape a nightmare.

Directions   Label the Sabine, Trinity, Brazos, and Colorado rivers on the map below. Then, using your textbook and the map, answer the questions that follow.

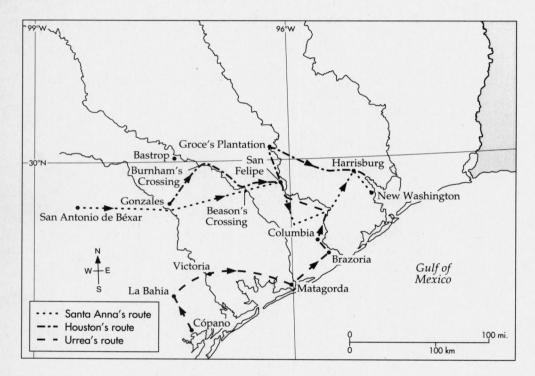

1. Where were families in the Runaway Scrape headed? _____
2. After Houston's retreat from Gonzales, what river did his army cross first?

   _____

3. After two weeks of drilling the Texas army, where did Houston cross the Brazos

   River? _____

4. Which army arrived at Harrisburg first? _____
5. When did Houston send word to Texans who fled in the Runaway Scrape that it

   was safe to return? _____

   _____

Texas Geography Skill 13

REGIONS: Texas Capitals

The first capital of the Republic of Texas was at Washington-on-the-Brazos. Texas, however, has had many locations for its government. In 1722, Spanish officials made Los Adaes (in Louisiana) the capital. It was moved in 1772 to San Antonio de Béxar, where it remained until 1824.

During the Texas Revolution, the site of government was moved several times to avoid capture by Santa Anna's troops. The location of the government was at Velasco, on the coast, when the treaties were signed that ended the fighting. In October 1836, the search for a permanent capital of Texas began.

Directions Using your textbook, complete the chart below on capitals of the Texas Republic.

Name of Town	Dates Used as Capital	Location	Reasons for Change
	September 1836 to April 1837		
	April 1837 to October 1839		
	October 1839 to the present		

Texas Geography Skill 14

For use with
Chapter 14
Life in the New Republic

HUMAN-ENVIRONMENT INTERACTION: New Settlements

During the years Texas was an independent republic, its population grew rapidly. Many of these settlers, chiefly those from Europe, were brought to Texas by immigrant agents.

Directions   Using your textbook, identify the settlement associated with each person named in the table below. Complete the table by writing the name of the settlement or its location, the letter marking its location, and the country of origin of the settler or immigrant agent. Finally, label each settlement on the map.

Name of Settler or Immigrant Agent	Area of Settlement or Town	Map Letter	Native Country
W. S. Peters			
John O. Meusebach		E	
Prince Carl of Solms-Braunfels	New Braunfels		
Henri Castro			
John Neely Bryan			
Henry L. Kenney			United States
George B. Erath			

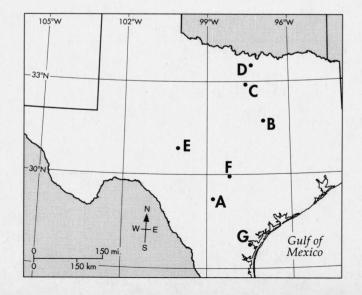

Texas Geography Skill 15

LOCATION: The Santa Fe Expedition

In 1841 Governor Lamar authorized an expedition of more than 300 soldiers to go to New Mexico for the purpose of expanding Texas territory to the Pacific. The expedition experienced many difficulties, was captured near Santa Fe, and marched to Mexico City. Many of the prisoners died along the route and in prison. The survivors were released in the spring of 1842.

Directions   The route of the Santa Fe expedition is shown in a bold dashed line on the outline map below. Use your textbook to label the cities of Austin, Santa Fe, and Mexico City. Label the Nueces River and Rio Grande. Shade the area disputed between Texas and Mexico. Then answer the questions that follow.

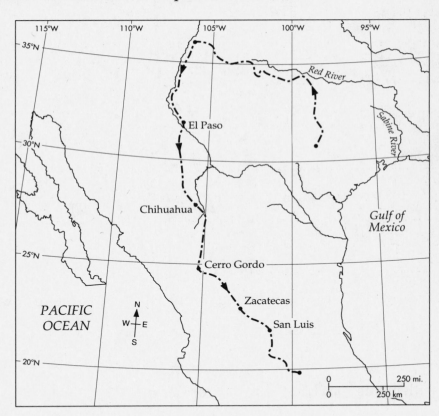

1. What direction did the expedition travel when it left Austin? _____

2. What Texas town did the prisoners march through on their way to Mexico?

_____

3. About how far was the march from Austin to Santa Fe? _____

4. About how far were the Santa Fe prisoners marched from Santa Fe to Mexico City?

_____

Texas Geography Skill 16

For use with
Chapter 16
Growth of the Young State

MOVEMENT: Immigrant Settlement

The population of Texas grew rapidly between 1830 and 1860.
Most of this increase was the result of immigration from the United
States, Mexico, and Europe.

Directions Study the outline map below showing immigration
into Texas. Then answer the questions that follow.

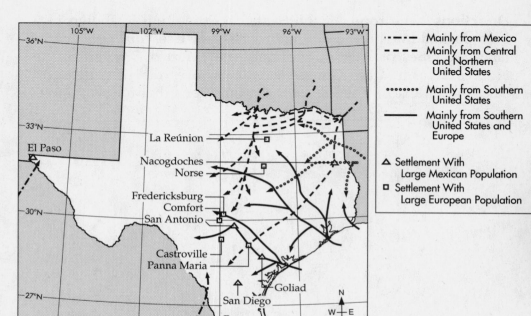

1. What was the origin of four major immigrant groups who came to Texas?

   _____

   _____

2. Name five settlements that had a large European population. _____

   _____

3. Name five settlements that had a large Mexican population. _____

   _____

4. What affect did the annexation of Texas to the United States have on immigration?

   _____

   _____

Texas Geography Skill 17

For use with
Chapter 17
Life in the New State

PLACE: Population in 1850

After Texas became a part of the United States in 1845, many immigrants who wanted a better way of life moved to the new state. The population in 1850 had climbed beyond 200,000.

Directions   Study the bar chart below on the population of Texas in 1850. Then answer the questions that follow.

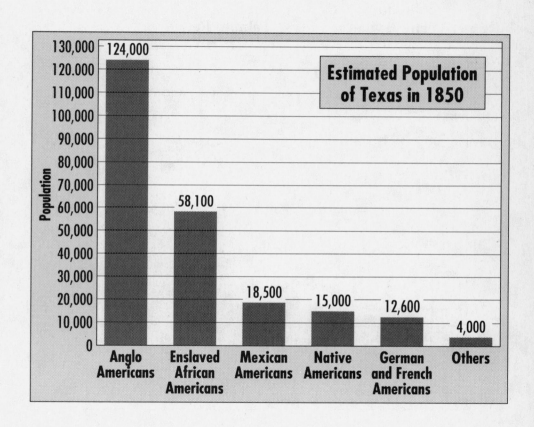

1. What cultural and ethnic groups are shown on this graph? _____

_____

_____

2. Which group made up the largest part of the population? _____

3. Which group made up the smallest part of the population? _____

4. The enslaved African American population in 1836 was about 5,000. How much

   had it increased by 1850? _____

5. Make an estimate of the total Texas population in 1850. _____

Texas Geography Skill 18

LOCATION: Civil War Texas

In 1861 Texas joined 10 other Southern states to form the Confederate States of America. During the Civil War that followed, Texas contributed significantly to the Confederate war effort.

Directions   Label the following places on the map below. Then answer the questions that follow.

Jefferson	Sabine Pass	Houston	Eagle Pass
Tyler	Laredo	Rusk	Galveston
Fredericksburg	Huntsville	Palmito Ranch	

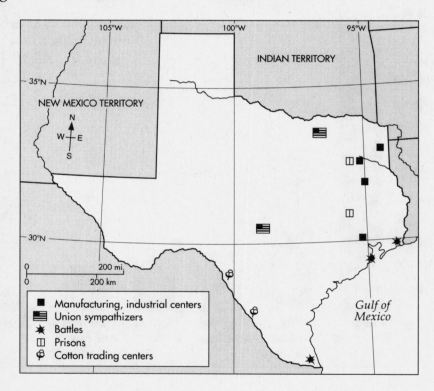

1. Where was cotton shipped into Mexico? _____

2. Name three sites where Civil War battles took place. _____

_____

3. Where were Confederate prisons located? _____

4. Name four industrial and manufacturing centers for the Confederacy. _____

_____

5. Where in Texas were there Union sympathizers? _____

_____

Texas Geography Skill 19

PLACE: Texas and Reconstruction

In 1866 Republicans in Congress took control of getting the Southern states back into the Union. They divided the South into five military districts and placed them under military commanders. Congress also required that the states approve the Fourteenth Amendment before they could rejoin the Union.

Directions   Study the map of Reconstruction below, then answer the questions that follow.

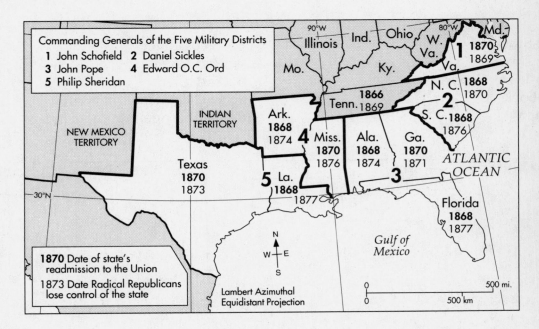

1. Who was the military commander in charge of the Texas-Louisiana district?

_____

2. When did Texas rejoin the Union? _____

3. What other Southern states reentered the Union the same year as Texas? _____

_____

_____

4. When did the Radical Republicans lose control of Texas? _____

5. When did the Radical Republicans lose control of Louisiana? _____

Texas Geography Skill 20

HUMAN-ENVIRONMENT INTERACTION: Frontier Campaigns

The Treaty of Medicine Lodge Creek in 1867 brought peace between Anglo settlers and many Native American groups. Some, however, including the Comanches, Kiowas, and Cheyenne, fought to protect their lands and way of life.

Directions Locate and label the following sites on the map below. Then, using the map legend, show the Trans-Pecos region and the area claimed by the Comanches and Kiowas.

1. Fort Stockton
2. Fort Davis
3. Palo Duro Canyon
4. Lubbock
5. Pampa

6. Pecos River
7. Red River
8. Fort Clark
9. Fort Concho
10. Saint Angelina

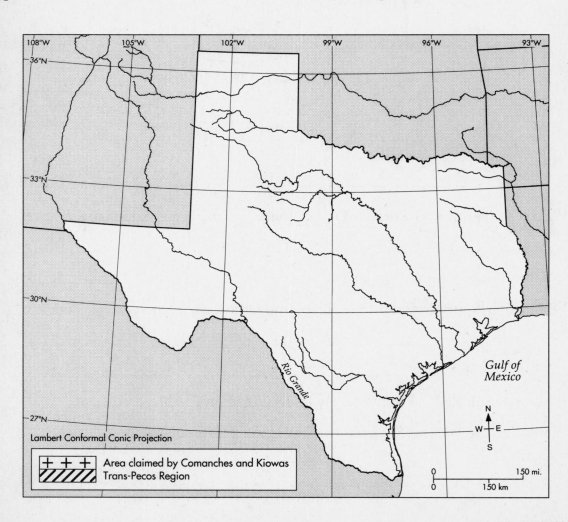

Lambert Conformal Conic Projection

Rio Grande

Gulf of Mexico

+ + + Area claimed by Comanches and Kiowas
/////// Trans-Pecos Region

0   150 mi.
0   150 km

Texas Geography Skill 21

REGIONS: Farm and Ranch Products

Texas became a prosperous agricultural state because of the development of its ranching and farming economy. Today Texas ranks second among the 50 states in the value of its ranch and farm products.

Directions   Study the map of Texas agricultural products below and answer the questions that follow.

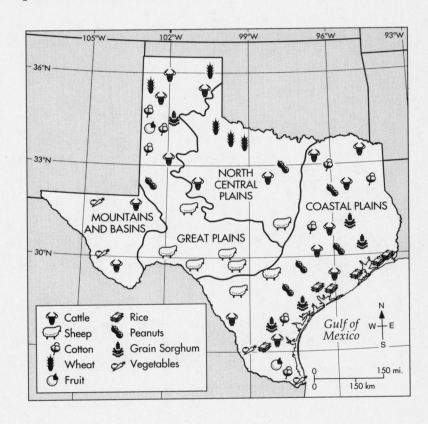

1. What farm products are produced in the Great Plains region? _____

   _____

2. What farm products are produced in the North Central Plains? _____

   _____

3. Which region of Texas has the widest range of farm products? What historical or

   environmental factors might explain this? _____

   _____

   _____

Texas Geography Skill 22

MOVEMENT: Texas Railroads

Railroad construction began in Texas in 1852. By 1900, nearly 9,838 miles of track connected various cities of the state.

Directions Use your textbook and the legend to label the six railroad lines on the map below. Then answer the questions that follow.

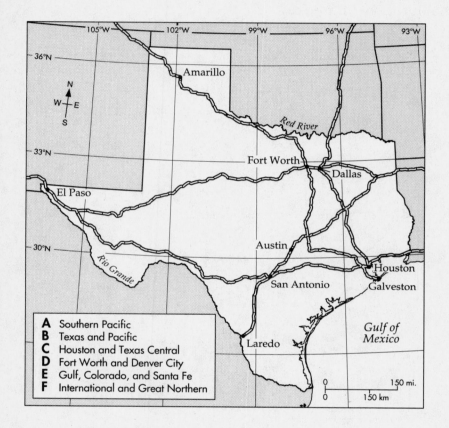

Legend:
A Southern Pacific
B Texas and Pacific
C Houston and Texas Central
D Fort Worth and Denver City
E Gulf, Colorado, and Santa Fe
F International and Great Northern

1. What railroad lines linked East Texas with West Texas? _____

   _____

2. Which railroads served cities in the Coastal Plains? _____

   _____

3. Which railroads could be used to ship goods from Del Rio to Austin? _____

   _____

4. Which railroad could be used to ship goods from the Red River to Houston?

   _____

5. Which railroad served cities in the Great Plains? _____

Texas Geography Skill 23

For use with
Chapter 23
The Oil Industry and a New Age

HUMAN-ENVIRONMENT INTERACTION: Crude Oil Production

The success of the Spindletop oil well in 1901 led to Texas becoming one of the top oil-producing states in the nation. Crude oil production reached its height in 1973 with 1,301,685,000 barrels.

Directions   Draw a line graph to show Texas crude oil production between 1915 and 1990. Use the data below to chart the graph. Then answer the questions that follow.

(bbl = barrels of crude oil, in thousands)

1915–24,943 bbl
1920–96,886 bbl
1925–144,648 bbl
1930–290,457 bbl
1935–392,666 bbl
1940–493,209 bbl

1945–754,710 bbl
1950–829,874 bbl
1955–1,053,297 bbl
1960–927,479 bbl
1965–1,000,749 bbl
1970–1,249,697 bbl

1975–1,221,929 bbl
1980–977,436 bbl
1985–860,300 bbl
1990–672,081 bbl

TEXAS CRUDE OIL PRODUCTION, 1915–1990

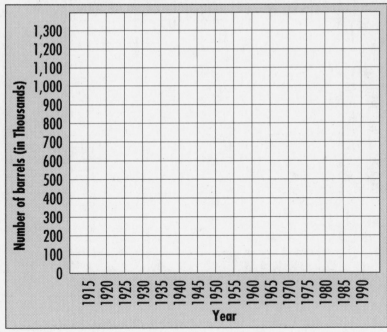

1. The largest increase in crude oil production took place during what five-year period? _____

2. In what year did crude oil production reach its peak? _____
3. The largest decrease of crude oil production took place during what five-year period? _____

Texas Geography Skill 24

For use with
Chapter 24
Emergence of a Modern State

PLACE: Texas Population Growth

Texas in the twentieth century has experienced remarkable population growth. In 1900 Texas was the fifth most populous state and by 1980 had climbed to third.

Directions Construct a bar graph that shows the population growth of Texas between 1900 and 1990, with estimated growth to the year 2010. Use the data and grid below to chart the graph. Then answer the questions that follow.

1900	3,034,710	1940	6,414,824	1980	14,228,383
1910	3,896,542	1950	7,711,194	1990	16,986,510
1920	4,663,228	1960	9,579,677	2000	20,211,000 (est.)
1930	5,824,715	1970	11,198,655	2010	22,281,000 (est.)

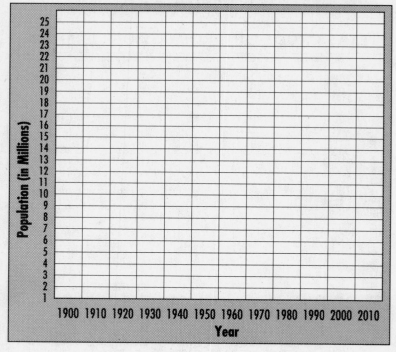

TEXAS POPULATION GROWTH, 1900–2010

1. How much did the population grow between 1900 and 1950? _____

   _____

2. How much did the population grow between 1950 and 1990? _____

   _____

3. In which decade did Texas experience the greatest population growth? _____

   _____

Texas Geography Skill 25

PLACE: Mexican American Cultural Influences

The Institute of Texan Cultures in San Antonio has identified 26 ethnic groups that have settled in Texas. Among the largest is the Mexican American. The influences of Mexico and the Hispanic culture of Latin America may be seen in nearly all parts of the state.

Directions Plan and conduct a treasure hunt for Mexican and Latin American influences in your community. Using the categories below, list examples of cultural influences that you can identify.

1. Names of popular foods

_____

_____

2. Names of local restaurants or restaurant chains

_____

_____

3. Clothing styles

_____

_____

4. Items purchased in stores

_____

_____

5. Names of cities, towns, or streets

_____

_____

6. Shared persons in history

_____

_____

7. Shared languages, religious faiths, and types of government

_____

_____

8. Holidays and celebrations

_____

_____

Texas Geography Skill 26

REGIONS: Texas Droughts

Droughts–long periods without rain–are harmful weather patterns. In Texas, droughts have led to a shortage of water for crops, industry, and human needs.

Directions   The following table shows the percentage of average annual rainfall for regions in Texas between 1910 and 1934. The Weather Bureau defines a drought as when an area receives less than 75 percent of its usual rainfall. Years not listed on the table indicate that all regions received at least 75 percent of their normal rainfall. Study the table, then answer the questions that follow.

PERCENTAGE OF NORMAL RAINFALL IN TEXAS DROUGHT YEARS, BY REGION

Year	Coastal Plains (45.5" av.)	North Central Plains (27.0" av.)	Great Plains (18.5" av.)	Mountains and Basins (12.0" av.)
1910	71	62	59	43
1911				70
1916	71	73		70
1917	55	51	58	44
1921				72
1924	72	72		
1925		72		
1927	74			
1933		68	72	62
1934		69	66	46

1. In which two years did drought conditions affect all regions of Texas? _____

2. In what year was the drought most severe? _____

3. In what year was the drought least severe? _____

4. What was the approximate average rainfall in the North Central Plains during 1925?

   (Hint: multiply the percent by the average) _____

5. Overall, which region in Texas was the least affected by drought conditions?

   _____

Texas Geography Skill 27

For use with
Chapter 27
Progress of a Modern State

LOCATION: Population Density

More than 17 million people live in Texas. Of the 50 states, Texas ranks third in population. The population, however, is distributed *unevenly* over the state. About 80 percent of all Texans live in urban areas, and about 70 percent live in the eastern half of the state. In 1990 Texas had an average population of about 65 persons per square mile. Some cities may have thousands of people per square mile, while isolated rural areas are virtually deserted.

Directions   Study the map showing the population density of Texas below. Then answer the questions that follow.

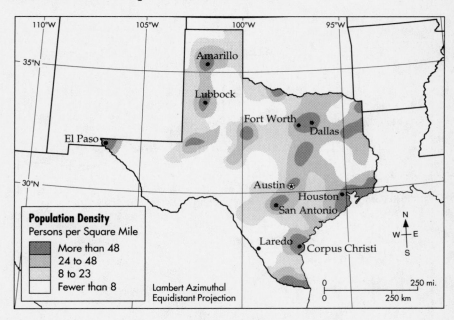

1. The largest area with more than 48 people per square mile is around what city?

_____

2. Do more people per square mile live around Lubbock or Laredo?

_____

3. How many people per square mile live between Austin and El Paso?

_____

4. How many people per square mile live between Dallas and Fort Worth?

_____

5. What happens to the population density as one moves away from a city?

_____

Texas Geography Skill 28

For use with
Chapter 28
Politics of a Modern State

MOVEMENT: Federal-State Cooperation

Texas has an excellent system of highways. Many of these highways were built by the United States government and the government of Texas working together. United States highways (known by their U.S. route number) are paid for equally by the state and federal government. Freeways or interstate highways, began to be built in Texas in the late 1950s. These modern highways are paid for with 90 percent federal funds and 10 percent Texas funds.

Directions Study the map of the interstate highway system in Texas shown below. Then answer the questions that follow.

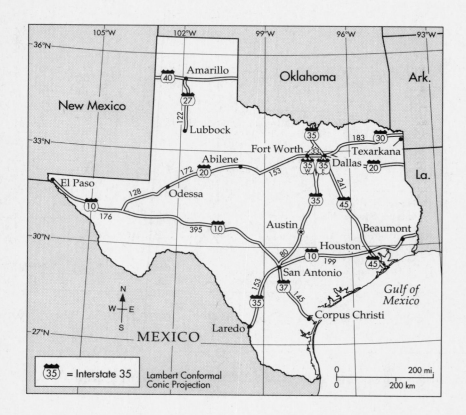

1. Which interstate connects Oklahoma with Mexico? _____

2. Which freeway connects New Mexico with Louisiana? _____

3. If you wanted to travel from Odessa to Houston, which interstates might you use?

   About how many miles is it? _____

4. If you were going from Corpus Christi to Austin, which freeways would you use? If you averaged traveling 55 miles per hour, about how long would the trip take?

Texas Geography Skill 29

REGIONS: Texas Trade with South Korea

Texas has a close economic relationship with many nations in Asia, particularly Japan, South Korea, and Taiwan. The evidence of trade between Texas and these countries is all around you in such products as cars, television sets, and clothing.

Directions   Using your textbook and other resources, learn about the trade between your community and South Korea. Use the information you find to complete the chart below.

TRADE BETWEEN YOUR COMMUNITY AND SOUTH KOREA

Korea Imports	Your Community Imports
Crude oil	
Wood products	
Machinery and equipment	
Metal ores	
Wheat, corn	
Chemicals	
Electronic components	
Plastics	
Korea Exports	**Your Community Exports**
Fertilizer	
Automobiles	
Television sets	
VCRs, Tape recorders	
Textiles	
Minerals	
Ships	
Iron ore	
Fish	

Texas Geography Skill 30

LOCATION: Visiting Historic Sites

The heritage of Texas developed over many centuries. An excellent way to learn about Texas is to visit historical sites where important events have taken place. Many historical sites have been restored.

Directions Using your textbook and an Official Texas Highway Travel Map, plan a trip that would take you from your home through all four natural regions of Texas. If possible, plan to visit at least two important historical sites in each region. Complete the chart below telling about the main things you would see on your trip. List the regions visited, highways used, and the sites visited in order.

Natural Region	Highways Traveled	Sites Visited	Points of Interest

NAME _____ DATE _____ CLASS _____

For use with
Chapter 31
The Texas Constitution
and System of Justice

Texas Geography Skill 31

REGIONS: Texas Counties

The state constitution provides for the creation of counties and makes them subdivisions of the state. At the time of Texas independence there were 23 counties. Today there are 254 counties, the last one created in 1931.

Directions   On the map below, use a pencil to shade in the county in which you live. Next trace the boundaries of the counties that border your county. Then use the map and the *Texas Almanac* to answer the questions below.

1. What is the name of your county seat (capital)? _____

2. When was your county created and how was it named? _____

_____

3. Of what Texas House and Senate districts is your county a part? _____

_____

Texas Geography Skill 32

PLACE: The Texas State Budget

A circle graph is an excellent tool to show how the size of budget items are related. For 1992 the Texas legislature approved a state budget of nearly $60 billion.

Directions Study the circle graph of the 1992 state budget below. Then answer the questions that follow.

THE 1992 TEXAS BUDGET

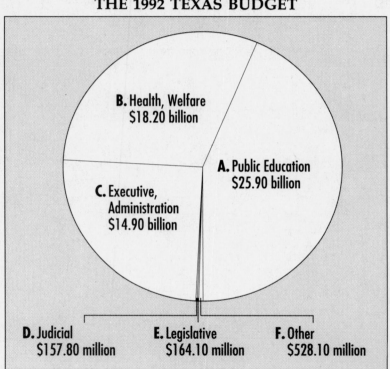

B. Health, Welfare
$18.20 billion

A. Public Education
$25.90 billion

C. Executive, Administration
$14.90 billion

D. Judicial
$157.80 million

E. Legislative
$164.10 million

F. Other
$528.10 million

1. What is the largest budget item and how many billions of dollars are reserved for it? _____

2. Which budget item receives about 25 percent of state funds? _____
_____

3. Which budget item is $157 million? _____

4. How many billion dollars does Health and Welfare receive? _____
_____

5. About how much is the total state budget for 1992? _____

Texas Geography Skill 33

REGIONS: Physical and Human Characteristics of Your Area

Texas is a diverse state. It has 254 counties and over 1,000 special district governments such as school boards and water districts. By learning about the physical and human characteristics of your area, you will be better able to participate in state and local government.

Directions Using your textbook and resources in your school's learning center, fill in the blanks about the geography of your area.

1. In which of the four natural regions of Texas do you live? _____

2. Name the important bodies of water in your area. _____

   _____

3. Describe the main types of natural vegetation that grow in your area. _____

   _____

4. Describe the climate in your area. Are the seasons hot or cold? Wet or dry? Windy

   or calm? _____

   _____

   _____

5. What important landforms are in or near your area? _____

   _____

6. Name the town or city in which you live. If you live in a rural area, what is your

   post office? _____

7. In what county do you live? What is the county seat? _____

8. What are some local places of interest that might attract tourists to your area?

   _____

9. List the name of your U.S. Representative to Congress, your Representative to the

   Texas House of Representatives, and your Texas State Senator. _____

   _____

10. In which school district do you live? Who is the district's school superintendent?

   _____

ANSWER KEY

CHAPTER 1, p. 1

Texas Geography Skill 1

1. southeast
2. north
3. northwest
4. 250 miles
5. 680 miles
6. 180 miles

CHAPTER 2, p. 2

Texas Geography Skill 2

1. D	6. L	11. M	16. A
2. S	7. J	12. B	17. O
3. P	8. G	13. E	18. K
4. R	9. F	14. Q	19. I
5. N	10. C	15. H	

CHAPTER 3, p. 3

Texas Geography Skill 3

North American Region	Texas Region	Major Cities
Western Mountains and Basins	Mountains and Basins	El Paso, Alpine, Pecos
Continental Interior Plain	Great Plains	Amarillo, Lubbock, Midland, San Angelo, Kerrville
	North Central Plains	Wichita Falls, Fort Worth, Abilene
Coastal Plain	Coastal Plains	Houston, Dallas, Austin, San Antonio, Brownsville

CHAPTER 4, p. 4

Texas Geography Skill 4

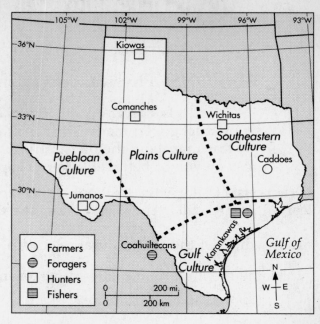

CHAPTER 5, p. 5

Texas Geography Skill 5

1. Cabeza de Vaca
2. Francisco Vasquez de Coronado
3. Alonso Álvarez de Piñeda
4. Karankawas, Coahuiltecans, and Jumanos
5. Caddo
6. fort, La Salle
7. Piney Woods
8. Coast
9. Palo Duro Canyon

CHAPTER 6, p. 6

Texas Geography Skill 6

Number	Settlement Name	Map Letter	Date Founded	Nearest River
1	Presidio San Antonio de Béxar	C	1718	San Antonio River
2	San Sabá de la Santa Cruz	B	1757	San Saba River
3	Nuestra Señora de Pilar de los Adaes	E	1722	Arroyo Hondo and Red rivers
4	San Francisco de los Tejas	D	1690	Neches River
5	Corpus Christi de la Ysleta	A	1682	Rio Grande

Texas Geography Skills

CHAPTER 7, p. 7

Texas Geography Skill 7

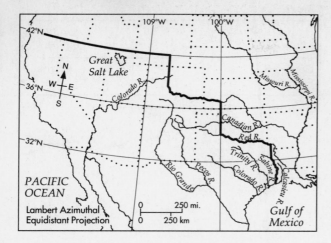

CHAPTER 8, p. 8

Texas Geography Skill 8

Date of Grant	Relative Location of Colony	Number of Families Settled
1823	Colorado and Brazos river valleys; coastal land between these rivers	300
1825	within boundaries of Austin's first grant	500
1827	East of the Colorado River, north of the San Antonio [Road]	100
1828	10 leagues from the Gulf coast	300
1831	large tract north and northwest of Austin's first colony	300

CHAPTER 9, p. 9

Texas Geography Skill 9

1. A
2. B
3. E
4. F
5. C
6. G
7. D
8. about 60 miles
9. Answers will vary but should include that Edwards appealed to the United States for help. The Fredonian Revolt was

another sign to Mexican officials that Americans were scheming to acquire Texas.

CHAPTER 10, p. 10

Texas Geography Skill 10

1. Gonzales, F
2. Goliad, E
3. San Felipe, B
4. San Antonio, A
5. Laredo, D
6. Harrisburg, C
7. Washington-on-the-Brazos, G

CHAPTER 11, p. 11

Texas Geography Skill 11

January 17, 1836 Bowie ordered to the Alamo by Houston
February 3, 1836 Arrival of Travis at Alamo garrison
February 23, 1836 First appearance of Santa Anna's troops at the Alamo
February 27, 1836 Defeat at San Patricio
March 3, 1836 Travis's last appeal to the Convention of 1836
March 6, 1836 Fall of the Alamo
March 12, 1836 Battle of Refugio
March 20, 1836 Battle of Coleto
March 27, 1836 Execution of Fannin and many of his soldiers

CHAPTER 12, p. 12

Texas Geography Skill 12

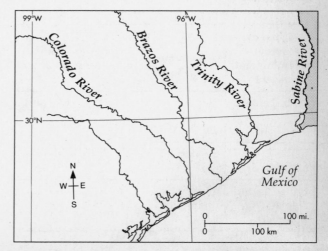

1. They wanted to cross the Sabine River into Louisiana.
2. the Colorado River
3. Groce's Plantation
4. Santa Anna's army reached Harrisburg first.
5. after the battle at San Jacinto and the capture of Santa Anna

CHAPTER 13, p. 13

Texas Geography Skill 13

Name of Town	Dates Used as Capital	Location	Reasons for Change
Columbia	September 1836 to April 1837	Brazoria County	To find a more central location with more places for people to stay
Houston	April 1837 to October 1839	On the Buffalo Bayou, five miles from Harrisburg in Harris County	Poor housing facilities; to find a site nearer to the population center of Texas
Austin (formerly Waterloo)	October 1839 to the present	On the Colorado River in present-day Travis County	None

CHAPTER 14, p. 14

Texas Geography Skill 14

Name of Settler or Immigrant Agent	Area of Settlement or Town	Map Letter	Native Country
W. S. Peters	Red River to south of Dallas	D	England
John O. Meusebach	Fredericksburg	E	Germany
Prince Carl of Solms-Braunsfeld	New Braunfels	F	Germany

Henri Castro	Castroville	A	France
John Neely Bryan	Dallas	C	United States
Henry L. Kenney	Corpus Christi	G	United States
George B. Erath	Waco	B	Austria

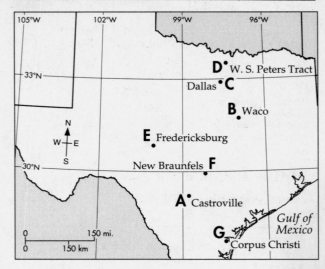

CHAPTER 15, p. 15

Texas Geography Skill 15

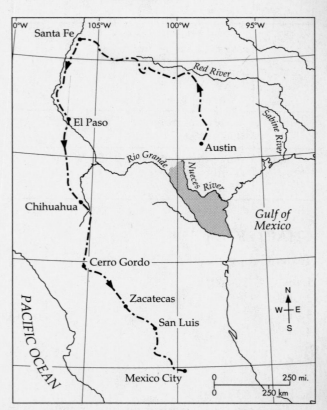

1. north
2. El Paso
3. about 700 miles
4. about 1000 miles

Copyright © by the Glencoe Division of Macmillan/McGraw-Hill School Publishing Company

CHAPTER 16, p. 16

Texas Geography Skill 16

1. Central and Northern United States, Southern United States, Southern United States and Europe, Mexico
2. La Réunion, Brownsboro, Norse, Fredericksburg, Comfort, Boerne, New Braunfels, Castroville, Panna Maria, Cat Spring, Praha
3. El Paso, Laredo, Roma, Goliad, San Antonio, Nacogdoches, Del Rio, San Diego, Brownsville
4. Answers will vary but students should understand that annexation as well as liberal land laws encouraged immigration. After annexation Americans could settle in Texas and retain their citizenship.

CHAPTER 17, p. 17

Texas Geography Skill 17

1. Anglo Americans; Enslaved African Americans; Tejanos; Native Americans; German and French Americans; and Others
2. Anglo Americans
3. Others
4. It increased by more than 53,000.
5. about 232,200

CHAPTER 18, p. 18

Texas Geography Skill 18

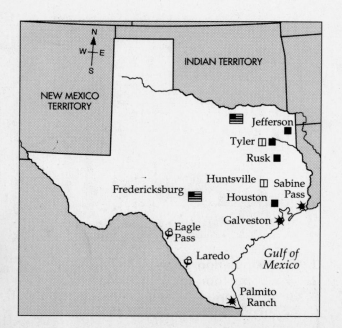

1. Laredo, Eagle Pass
2. Sabine Pass, Galveston, Palmito Ranch
3. Tyler, Huntsville
4. Hunt, Jefferson, Tyler, Houston
5. Fredericksburg, Collin County and other counties along the Red River

CHAPTER 19, p. 19

Texas Geography Skill 19

1. Philip Sheridan
2. 1870
3. Mississippi, Georgia, and Virginia
4. 1873
5. 1877

CHAPTER 20, p. 20

Texas Geography Skill 20

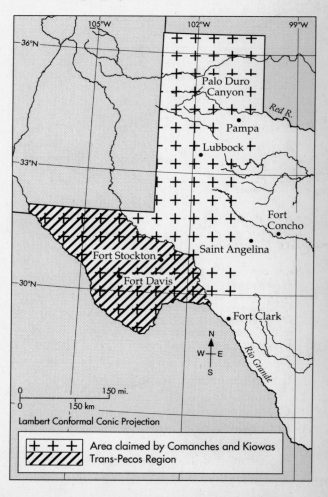

CHAPTER 21, p. 21

Texas Geography Skill 21

1. cattle, sheep, wheat, grain sorghum, fruit, cotton, and peanuts
2. sheep, cattle, wheat, and peanuts
3. Coastal Plains; This was the first area of Texas to be settled and has a longer history of agricultural development. The climate of the Coastal Plains is wetter and warmer than the other regions. This allows a wide variety of agricultural products to be grown.

CHAPTER 22, p. 22

Texas Geography Skill 22

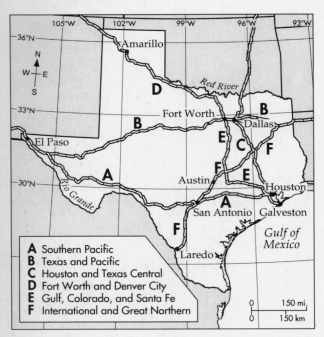

1. Southern Pacific; Texas Pacific
2. Houston and Texas Central; Gulf, Colorado and Santa Fe; Southern Pacific
3. Southern Pacific; and International and Great Northern
4. Houston and Texas Central
5. Fort Worth and Denver City

CHAPTER 23, p. 23

Texas Geography Skill 23

TEXAS CRUDE OIL PRODUCTION, 1915–1990

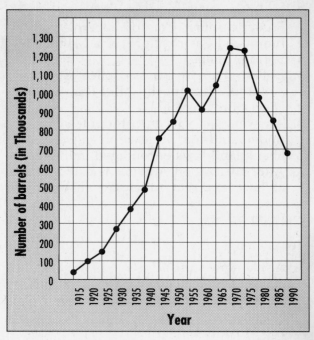

1. 1940–1945   2. 1970   3. 1975–1980

CHAPTER 24, p. 24

Texas Geography Skill 24

TEXAS POPULATION GROWTH, 1900–2010

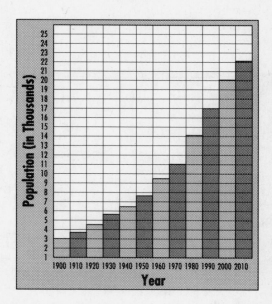

1. The population grew by 4,676,484.
2. The population grew by 9,348,611.
3. In the decade between 1980 and 1990 the population grew by 2,831,422.

CHAPTER 25, p. 25

Texas Geography Skill 25

1. Answers will vary. Tacos, burritos, tortillas, and enchiladas are popular.
2. Answers will vary; consult the yellow pages of your local phone directory for possibilities. Taco Bell and El Chico are two national chains.
3. Answers will vary. Two examples are colorful Mexican dresses and the guayabera, or wedding shirt. Ponchos and chaps are still worn in ranch work.
4. Answers will vary. Many clothing items are manufactured in Mexico and Latin America. Fresh fruits, vegetables, and dried flowers are other common imported items.
5. Answers will vary. Consult a Texas highway map or local city directory for Spanish place names.
6. Answers will vary. Until 1836 Mexico and Texas shared a common history; any significant person prior to the Texas Revolution is acceptable. Other people might include Ignacio Zaragoza, Joel Poinsett, and Doreteo Arango (Pancho Villa).
7. Spanish; Roman Catholicism is the major religion in Mexico and the largest single church body in Texas; both Texas and Mexico operate under a democratic constitution with republican forms of government.
8. Answers will vary. Many Texans celebrate Cinco de Mayo, Diez y Seis de Septiembre, and other Mexican holidays. Many Mexican American girls have fifteenth-birthday parties that signify their coming of age.

CHAPTER 26, p.26

Texas Geography Skill 26

1. 1910 and 1917
2. 1917
3. 1927
4. 19.44 inches
5. the Great Plains region

CHAPTER 27, p. 27

Texas Geography Skill 27

1. Houston
2. Lubbock
3. fewer than 8
4. more than 48
5. The density of the population decreases.

CHAPTER 28, p. 28

Texas Geography Skill 28

1. I-35
2. I-10
3. I-20, I-45; 400 miles
4. I-37, I-35; The distance is about 190 miles. At 55 miles per hour, the trip would take about 3.45 hours, or 3 hours, 26 minutes.

CHAPTER 29, p. 29

Texas Geography Skill 29

In the chart, answers for products that your local community imports and exports will vary. If your community has only one or two exports such as grain or vegetables, you may expand "community" to include a wider region of Texas.

CHAPTER 30, p. 30

Texas Geography Skill 30

Answers will vary. Check to make sure students label each natural region correctly, that appropriate highways are used, and that at least two sites are listed in each region.

CHAPTER 31, p. 31

Texas Geography Skill 31

All answers will vary. Make sure that students have correctly identified their county and the counties that border it. See the Texas Almanac (1992–1993), pages 181–320 for information of each Texas county and Texas House and Senate districts.

CHAPTER 32, p. 32

Texas Geography Skill 32

1. Public Education, $25.90 billion
2. Executive, Administration
3. Judicial
4. $18.20 billion
5. $59.85 billion

CHAPTER 33, p. 33

Texas Geography Skill 33

Answers for Questions 1–10 will vary. Students may want to consult a Texas highway map, the Texas Almanac, and local newspapers for information.